NEFRET'S
WHITE
DRESS
WITH
COLORED
SASHES

RAMSES
THE EMEF

AMELIA'S
RATIONALS
WITH
DIVIDED
SKIRT

EMERSON'S EXCAVATION
OUTFIT

EMERSON'S FROCK SUIT WORN
WITH TOP HAT OR TURBAN

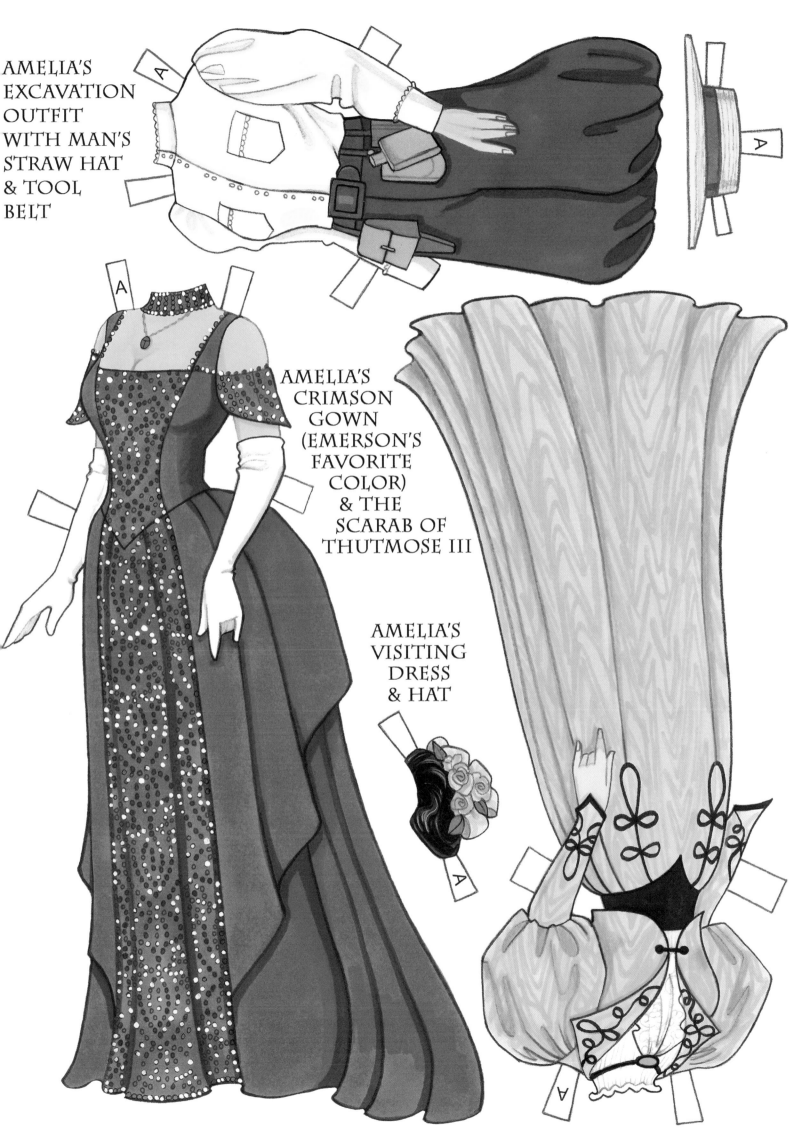

AMELIA'S
EXCAVATION
OUTFIT
WITH MAN'S
STRAW HAT
& TOOL
BELT

AMELIA'S
CRIMSON
GOWN
(EMERSON'S
FAVORITE
COLOR)
& THE
SCARAB OF
THUTMOSE III

AMELIA'S
VISITING
DRESS
& HAT

NEFRET'S PINK
TEA DRESS

RAMSES' EXCAVATION
ATTIRE WITH
PITH HELMET

AMELIA'S
EXCAVATION
OUTFIT

NEFRET'S
PRIESTESS
OF ISIS

AMELIA'S
PARASOL &
BOOTS FOR
EXCAVATING

RAMSES'
SAILOR SUIT

AMELIA'S
LAVENDER
EXCAVATION
OUTFIT

N

R

R

A

A

A

A

cut
out

EMERSON'S THOTH MASK & ROBE   EXORCISM ROBE & CAP

STREET ARAB RAMSES

AMELIA'S
SEKHMET MASK
& ROBE

NEFRET'S
NUBIAN ROBE

BASTET

RAMSES' KILT & PECTORAL

R

R

E

EMERSON'S KILT,
NECK COLLAR
& HEAD CIRCLET

E

E

ANUBIS

A

AMELIA'S ROBE &
COIFFURE